BLOW A KISS, CATCH A KISS

Joseph Coelho   Nicola Killen

Andersen Press

For the adults taking time to read to their little poets – you rock – J.C.

For Jess, Hugues, Gabriel and Melody – N.K.

First published in Great Britain in 2022 by Andersen Press Ltd.,
20 Vauxhall Bridge Road, London SW1V 2SA, UK
Vijverlaan 48, 3062 HL Rotterdam, Nederland
Text copyright © Joseph Coelho 2022
Illustration copyright © Nicola Killen 2022
The rights of Joseph Coelho and Nicola Killen to be identified as the
author and illustrator of this work has been asserted by them in
accordance with the Copyright, Designs and Patents Act, 1988.
All rights reserved. Printed and bound in China.
1 3 5 7 9 10 8 6 4 2
British Library Cataloguing in Publication Data available.
ISBN 978 1 83913 136 3

ALL ABOUT ME

Faces

Big face.
Little face.
Happy face.
Crazy face.

Big-little face.
Happy-crazy face.

Little-happy face.
Big-crazy face.

Crazy-little face.
Happy-big face.

Face, face, face, faces.

Hairy

Straight hair.
Curly hair.
Shake your hair.
Bear hair!

Eye Caterpillars

Eyebrows up.

Eyebrows down.

Eyebrows wiggle.

Eyebrows frown.

My Favourite Food

My favourite fruits are apples. Crunch!
My favourite drink is tea. Sip!

I like to munch on apples
and I love a pot of tea. Crunch! Sip!

My favourite cake is rock. Bite!
My favourite sandwich is jam. Yum!

I like to bite on rock cakes
and get yummy with some jam. Bite! Yum!

My favourite veg is carrot. Snap!
My favourite pudding is jelly. Wobble!

I like to snap a carrot
and get wobbly with jelly. Snap! Wobble!

Brilliant 'O'

I can waggle my ears
and I can twitch my nose
I can turn my mouth
into a great big 'O'.

I can steeple my fingers
and interlace my toes
I can bend my legs
to form a super 'O'.

I can click my tongue
and crouch down low
I can lift my arms
to form a brilliant 'O'.

Baby Exercise

Stretch up high,
now touch your toes.
Wiggle your belly,
wiggle your nose.
Make a star,
now scrunch up small.
Blow out your cheeks
like two beachballs.

The Nose Boogie

Scrunch your nose
wiggle your nose
blow your nose
smell with your nose.

Scrunch your nose
wiggle your nose
blow your nose
extend your nose.

Scrunch your nose
wiggle your nose
blow your nose
smell your toes.

BIG Mouth

Make your mouth big
now make your mouth small
blow out your cheeks
now huff, puff blow!

Huff, puff blow,
huff, puff blow,
huff, puff blow
like wind and snow.

Give me a smile
now a great big roar
stick out your tongue
now sleep and snore.

Sleep and snore,
sleep and snore,
sleep and snore,
give a great big ROAR!

Kissable Cheeks

I have kissable cheeks,
unmissable cheeks,
cheeky cheek cheeks.
Won't you take a peek
at my kissable cheeks,
unmissable cheeks,
cheeky cheek cheeks.
Grandma pinching,
aunty kissing,
you're all missing
my cheeks.

Collecting

I like to keep things
and put them in my pockets,
tiny things, little things
I put them in my pockets,
a tiny little twig,
a little toy rocket,
a small green leaf,
I put them in my pockets.

I like to collect things
and put them in a box,
lovely things, jubbly things
I put them in a box,
the depth of the sky,
the height of my block,
the width of the trees,
I put them in a box.

I like to gather things
and put them on a shelf,
sticky things, icky things
I put them on a shelf,
a dollop of troll slime,
some earwax from an elf,
a giant's giant bogie,
I put them on a shelf.

OUT AND ABOUT

The Journey Game

When you see a tree say…
Treetreetree.

When you see a cow say…
Moomoomoo.

When you see a red car say…
Oooooh la la!

When you see a blue car say…
Weeeeeooooooow.

When you see a cloud say
What'cha doing up there?
What'cha doing up there?
How did ya get so high
High up in the air?

Shopping Adventure

Gliding in the trolley
to the land between the shelves,
looking out for the magical things
like the fruit and vegetable elves.

Riding in the trolley
past the walls of cans,
looking out for the magical things
like the smiling silver-can man.

Winding in the trolley
to pay for all our things,
listening out for the invisible birds
that ping as they sing.

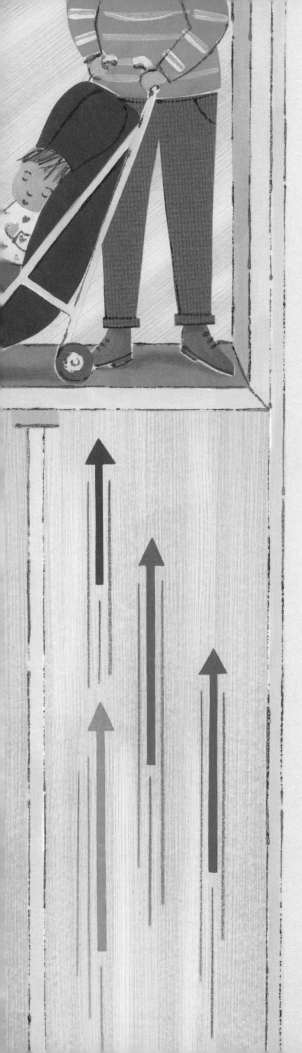

Uplifting

The lift goes up.
Up up up.
The lift goes down.
Down down down.

The lift goes sideways.
"Oh no it doesn't!"
The lift goes diagonally.
"Oh no it doesn't!"

The lift goes up.
Up up up.
The lift goes down.
Down down down.

Weather

The wind has got his scarf on
he is blowing through the land.
The wind has got his scarf on
sounding like a big brass band.

The rain has got her boots on
and now it is wet-play.
The rain has got her boots on
splashing puddles of silver-grey.

The snow has got her gloves on,
she is sliding on her sleigh.
The snow has got her gloves on
wrapping a blanket around the day.

The sun has got his shine on.
We are warmed by a star.
The sun has got his shine on
sending his love so very far.

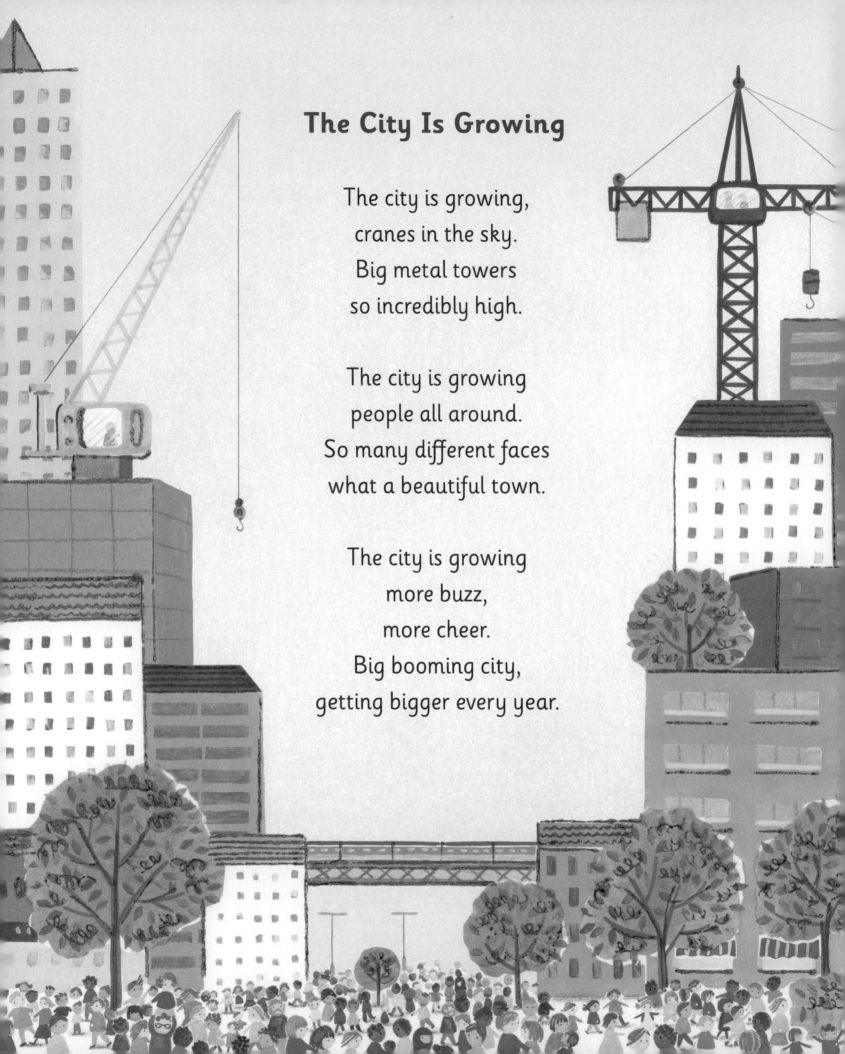

The City Is Growing

The city is growing,
cranes in the sky.
Big metal towers
so incredibly high.

The city is growing
people all around.
So many different faces
what a beautiful town.

The city is growing
more buzz,
more cheer.
Big booming city,
getting bigger every year.

Pigeons

Pigeons fly and swoop and soar
land and peck
and peck some more.

Their feathers hide a cunning secret.
A fantastic surprise can you see it?
Some say their feathers
are grey and black,
but look again – it's a colour attack!

Their feathers are green and purple
silver and pink,
A rainbow of feather-colour shines
as they peck and drink.

Hide The Jelly

Press the button, swipe the screen.
Ring the bell, drop the bean.
Hide the jelly on the train.
Take a flight on a plane.

Walk Like A Crocodile

Walk to school
like a crocodile.

Holding hands,
tight tight tight.

Walk to school
with a great big smile.

Show your teeth,
bright bright bright.

The Whooshing Wind

The wind is blowing me
up the hill.

Whdrooooshing me.
The wind is blowing me
up the hill.

Whrooooshing me.

The wind is blowing me up the hill
it will not stop,
I can't stand still,
The wind is blowing me up the hill.

Same Difference

Different faces,
    same smiles.

Different hairstyles,
    same hairdresser.

Different skin,
    same goosebumps.

Different arms,
    same hug.

Different jokes,
    same laugh.

Different parents,
    same love.

WHAT DO I FEEL?

Blow A Kiss

Blow a kiss,
catch a kiss
when we are apart.

Blow a kiss,
catch a kiss
put it in your heart.

Look I'm Happy

Look! I'm happy!
Happy! Happy! Happy!

Now I'm sad!
Boo! Hoo! Hoo!

Look I'm scared!
What's that? What's that? What's that?

Now I'm mad!
Bang! Bang! Bang!

But look… now I'm happy!
Happy! Happy! Happy!

Smiling like the sun.
Happy! Happy! Happy!

Stretching my arms wide.
Happy! Happy! Happy!

Feeling warm inside.
Happy! Happy! Happy!

Counting To Ten

Feeling angry.
Just count to ten.
Feeling mad.
Just count to ten.
Feeling annoyed.
Just count to ten...

One, two, three, four, five, six, seven, eight, nine, ten.

Feeling calm,
I just counted to ten.
Feeling kind,
I just counted to ten.
Feeling happy,
I just counted to ten.

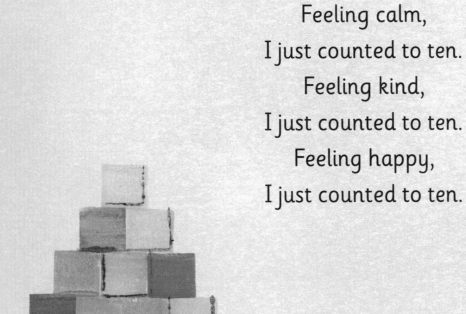

The Blues

I've got the blues,
I caught the blues,
I'm feeling sad
what should I do?

I'm feeling blue
from toe to top.
I'm feeling low,
I'm in a strop.

I wasn't blue this morning
and yesterday I felt glad
but now I've got the blues.
Now I feel a bit sad.

Give me a cuddle
and some warm cocoa.
Tell me a joke,
tickle my toe-toe.

Blow a raspberry on my belly,
put my favourite show on the telly,
give me a bowl of strawberry jelly
let me splash in my frog wellies.

Anger

Anger came a-bubbling,
a-bubbling, a-bubbling.

Anger came a-doubling,
a-doubling, a-doubling.

Anger came a-shuggerling,
a-shuggerling, a-shuggerling.

Anger came a-nuggerling,
a-nuggerling, a-nuggerling.

A-nuggerling, a-shuggerling,
a-doubling, a-bubbling,

a-bibberling, a-dibberling,
a-dinkerling, a-clinkerling

anger is a-shrinkerling,
a-smallering, a-plinkerling

and now I am a-giggling
a-giggling, a-giggling.

This Is...

This is fear,
tiny little fear.
Not a smile on his face
not a grin, not a cheer.

This is joy,
happy, laughing joy.
Chuckling like a rainbow
as playful as a toy.

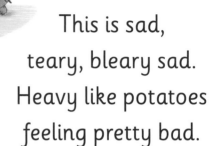

This is sad,
teary, bleary sad.
Heavy like potatoes
feeling pretty bad.

This is happy,
smiling, sparkling happy.
Always a bounce in her step
always feeling chatty.

A Rainbow Of Feelings

I have a rainbow inside me
every day new colours appear.
Sometimes red and angry.
I have a rainbow inside me.

Sometimes green with envy,
sometimes yellow with fear.
I have a rainbow inside me,
every day new colours appear.

Hot And Cold

Through the cold and the rain
I am shivering.
Through the hail and wind
I am snivelling.

My teeth are chattering
and my knees are knocking.
The ice is shattering,
this weather is shocking.

Through the sun and heat
I am sweating.
Through the rays and shine
I am burning.

My eyes are squinting
and my skin is pouring.
The sun is glaring
this weather gets me snoring.

Stomp, Sneak, Dance

Anger goes...
Stomp, stomp, **stomping**
Through the rocky mountains.

Fear goes...
Sneak, sneak, sneaking
Through the deep, dark woods.

Love goes...
Dance, dance, **dancing**
Through the flowery meadows.

Some Words

Some words are spiky
all edges and points.

Some words are fluffy
all soft and feather.

Some words come fast
and hurt when they land.

Some words come slow
and stroke and soothe.

Some words float and bounce and pop.
Some words droop and sag and flop.

Some words flicker and rage like fire.
Some words tinkle and gurgle like water.

Some words purr
and some words growl.
Some words creep and stalk and howl.

Some words are magic and some words are foul.
Some words should not be spoken.
Some words should be yelled out loud.

Take A Deep Breath

Close your eyes,
imagine the sea.

Take a deep breath...
and let it out.

Close your eyes,
imagine the waves splashing your feet.

Take a deep breath...
and let it out.

Close your eyes,
imagine your toes in the sand.

Take a deep breath...
and let it out.

Close your eyes,
imagine the sun on your face.

Take a deep breath...
and let it out.

Give A Friend A Hug

Give a friend a hug
when they're feeling sad,
give a friend two hugs
to make them feel quite glad.

Give a friend three hugs
and now they are laughing,
give a friend four hugs
and now they are dancing.

Give a friend five hugs
and flowers pop out of their hair!
Give a friend six hugs
and now they're whizzing through the air.

Give a friend seven hugs
and they shine like starlight!
Give a friend eight hugs
and they become a dazzling sight.

Give a friend nine hugs,
hold them tight like a bear.
Give a friend ten hugs,
show them that you care.

AT HOME

Dancing Families

Mum and Dad are dancing,
baby can't stop laughing
when Mum and Dad are dancing.

Mum is wiggling,
baby can't stop giggling
when Mum gets to wiggling.

Dad is sliding,
baby is a-gliding
when Dad gets to sliding.

Mum and Ma are twirling,
baby can't stop swirling
when Mum and Ma are twirling.

Dad and Pa are spinning,
baby can't stop grinning
when Dad and Pa are spinning.

Ma and Pa are bopping,
baby's eyes are popping
when Ma and Pa are bopping.

Smile Throwing

Throw a smile
across the room,
someone catches it
they smile back.

Throw two smiles
to opposite sides.
Two people catch them
they pass them on.

Two people throw two smiles
and now there are four.
Four smiles are caught
and thrown some more.

Now there are eight smiles...
Oops! I mean sixteen.
Smiles are spreading.
A smiley dream.

Family ON

Mum's on
the computer.
Brother's on
the telly.
Dad's on
the internet.
I'm on
the toilet.

Hand On Love

Hand on head.
Hand on tummy.
Hand on nose.
Hand on Mummy.

Bubble Pop

In the bath
I have a beard of bubbles,
bold bubbling bubbles
all over my chin.

In the bath
I pop my beard of bubbles,
popping plopping bubbles,
all over my chin.

In the bath
I have a beehive hairdo of bubbles,
beautiful bubbling bubbles,
all over my head.

In the bath
I pop my beehive hairdo of bubbles,
popping plopping bubbles,
all over my head.

In the bath
I have a backpack of bubbles,
big bubbling bubbles,
all over my back.

In the bath
I pop my backpack of bubbles,
popping, plopping bubbles
all over my back.

Arty

Hands on paint,
hands on paper.
Make a painting of
splatter,
splatter,
splatter.

Hands in water,
hands on clay.
Make a model of
squidge,
squeeze,
squeeze.

Fingers on screen,
fingers tap app.
Make a picture of
swipe,
swipe,
swipe.

Take A Book From The Shelf

Take a book from the shelf
and flip to the sea –
I'm a pirate captain,
"Ay ay mateys."

Take a book from the shelf
and flip to the woods –
I'm a bear eating honey,
"This honey is good."

Take a book from the shelf
and flip to the stars –
I'm zooming through space,
"Next stop Mars!"

Take a book from the shelf
and flip through the pages.
Get lost in adventures
for ages and ages...

Pick It Up!

I like to pick stuff up
          and put it over there
anywhere, everywhere
          I don't really care.

I pick it up,
I lift it up,
I move it and I stack it.

Don't know where it is?
I moved it and I packed it.

Underneath the sofa,
scattered on the rug.
I picked it up and moved it
then I found you for a hug.

That tiny precious thing
that you never want to lose,
I picked it up, held it up,
and left it in your shoes.

That stuff you're always putting
all over your face,
I picked it up, held it up,
sent it to outer space.

Under My Spell

Under the table,

    a dragon in its lair.

Under the bed

    in a comfy submarine.

Under the stairs,

    in a pirate's cabin.

Under an umbrella,

    in a jungle waterfall.

Under the weather,

    a sneezing flower fairy.

Under the covers,

    being treated by the elves.

Avocado! Avocado!

Avocado! Avocado!
Baby loves his avocado.
Avocado – let's go bravo!
As baby eats his avocado!

Avocado, green and creamy.
Avocado, tastes so dreamy!
Avocado! Avocado!
Baby loves his avocado.

I Love You

I love you little,
I love you tall,
I love you big,
I love you all.

I love each toe
on each little foot,
I love you like...
tree loves root,
like cake loves party,
like rain loves splat.
I love you.
You love me back.

Dreamtime

Turn off the screen!
put down the phone,
turn the TV down,
put the radio on low.

Unplug the console,
stop the toy from zapping,
dim the lights,
get ready for napping.

Lie on the floor
and look to the ceiling,
roll into a ball
and do some deep breathing.

Stretch yourself long,
curl up like a snail,
roll onto your tummy
pretend you have a tail.

Close your eyes tight,
have a deep yawn,
get ready for sweet dreams
what adventures will you go on?

Crawl into bed,
hug your covers tight,
sink into your pillow.
What a beautiful night.

Close your eyes tight,
smile as you doze
give yourself a hug
relax your fingers and your toes.

Now you are a-travelling
to the land of all your dreams,
I'll come see you in the morning
and you can tell me what you've seen.